Parts of the Ukulele

Soundhole

Rose

Strings

Saddle

Bridge

Neck

Tuning peg

Fingerboard

Frets

Fret marker

Body

Bout

Side

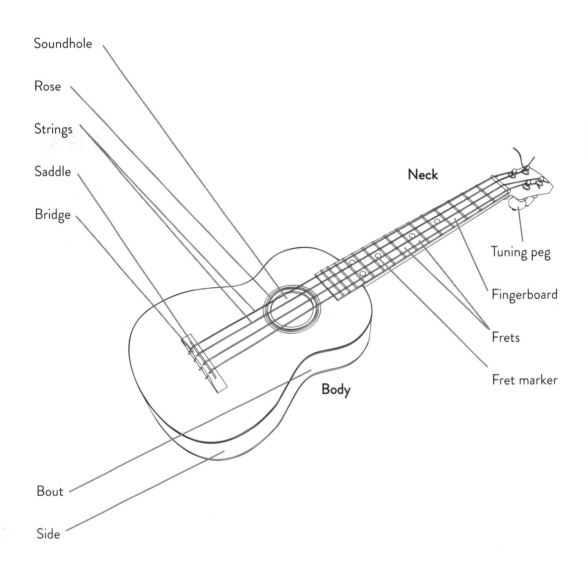

the ukuleles

Wise Publications
part of The Music Sales Group

London / New York / Paris / Sydney / Copenhagen / Berlin / Madrid / Hong Kong / Tokyo

Published by
Wise Publications
14-15 Berners Street, London W1T 3LJ, UK.

Exclusive Distributors:
Music Sales Limited
Distribution Centre, Newmarket Road, Bury St Edmunds, Suffolk IP33 3YB, UK.
Music Sales Pty Limited
20 Resolution Drive, Caringbah, NSW 2229, Australia.

Order No. AM1005675
ISBN: 978-1-78038-783-3
This book © Copyright 2012 Wise Publications,
a division of Music Sales Limited.

Edited by Adrian Hopkins.
Music arranged by Matt Cowe.
Music processed by Paul Ewers Music Design.
Original CD design by Oink Creative.
Cover photographs: joelanderson.com

With thanks to Logan Wilson, Martha Paton,
Jeff Chegwin and Nick Patrick.

DVD produced by Jonas Persson.

Printed in the EU.

Your Guarantee of Quality:

As publishers, we strive to produce every book
to the highest commercial standards.

This book has been carefully designed to minimise awkward
page turns and to make playing from it a real pleasure.

Particular care has been given to specifying acid-free, neutral-sized paper
made from pulps which have not been elemental chlorine bleached. This pulp is from
farmed sustainable forests and was produced with special regard for the environment.

Throughout, the printing and binding have been planned to ensure a sturdy,
attractive publication which should give years of enjoyment.

If your copy fails to meet our high standards, please inform us
and we will gladly replace it.

www.musicsales.com

Tuning the Ukulele

The ukulele is unusual among string instruments in that the strings are not tuned in order of pitch. Watch out for this!

Here are tuning notes for the ukulele on a piano keyboard:

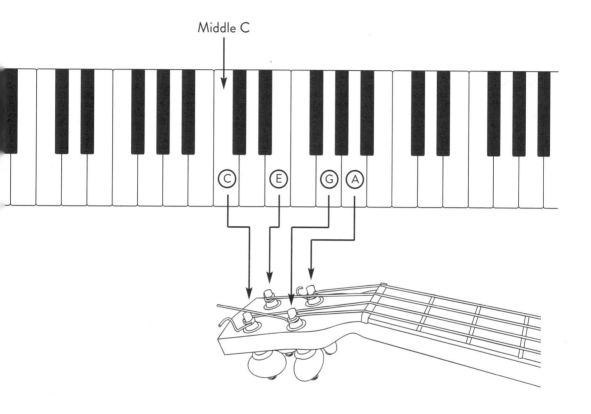

A good way to remember the notes of the ukulele's strings is this little tune:

My   dog   has   fleas!

Forget You

Words & Music by Christopher Brown, Thomas Callaway,
Ari Levine, Philip Lawrence & Peter Hernandez

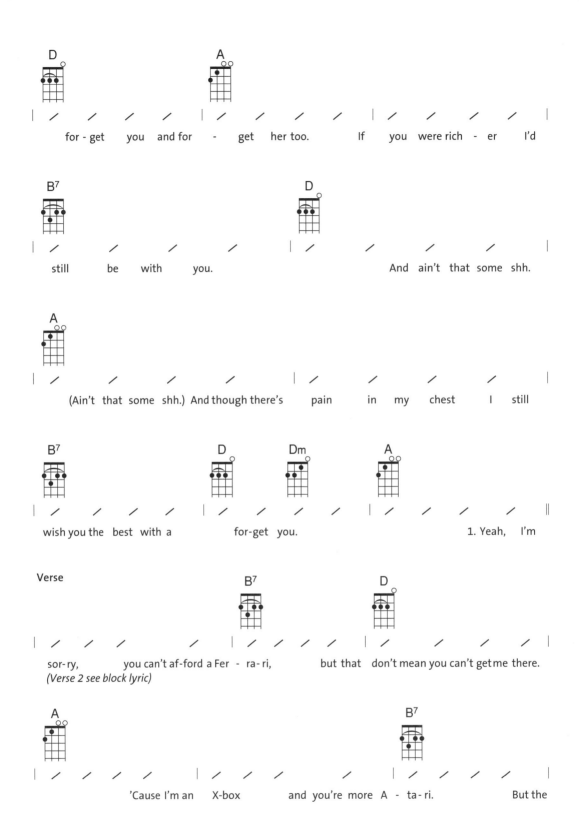

D   A

/   /   /   / | /   /   /   / | /   /   /   /

for - get   you   and for   -   get   her too.   If   you   were rich - er   I'd

B⁷   D

still   be   with   you.   And   ain't   that   some   shh.

A

(Ain't   that   some   shh.) And though there's   pain   in   my   chest   I   still

B⁷   D   Dm   A

wish you the   best   with a   for-get   you.   1. Yeah,   I'm

Verse   B⁷   D

sor-ry,   you can't af-ford a Fer - ra-ri,   but that   don't mean you can't get me there.
(Verse 2 see block lyric)

A   B⁷

'Cause I'm an   X-box   and you're more A - ta-ri.   But the

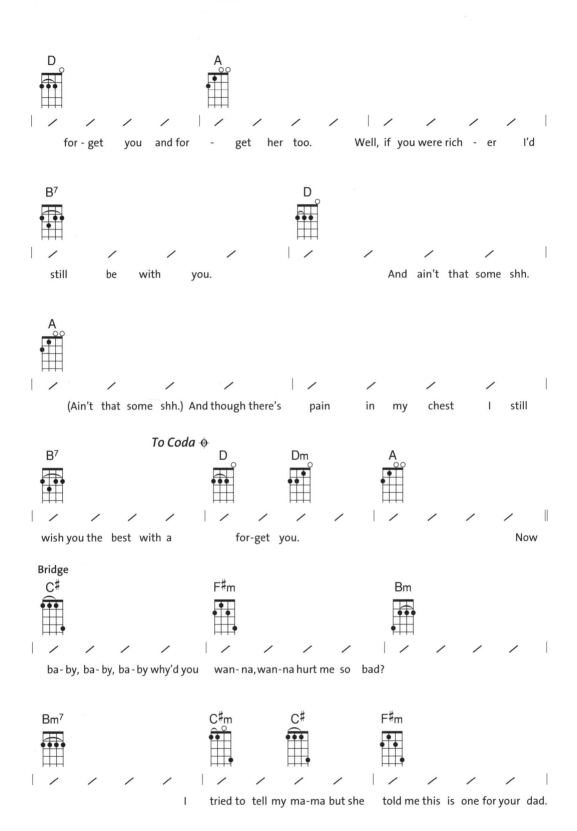

D | **A**

for - get you and for - get her too. Well, if you were rich - er I'd

B⁷ | **D**

still be with you. And ain't that some shh.

A

(Ain't that some shh.) And though there's pain in my chest I still

To Coda ⊕

B⁷ | **D** **Dm** | **A**

wish you the best with a for-get you. Now

Bridge

C♯ | **F♯m** | **Bm**

ba - by, ba - by, ba - by why'd you wan- na, wan-na hurt me so bad?

Bm⁷ | **C♯m** **C♯** | **F♯m**

I tried to tell my ma-ma but she told me this is one for your dad.

10

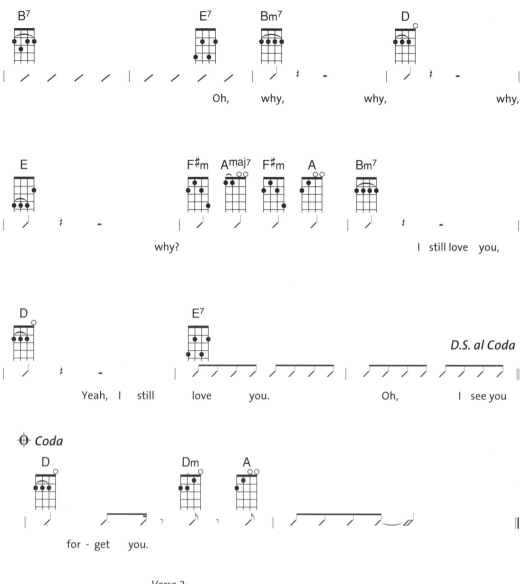

Oh,   why,   why,   why,

why?   I still love you,

Yeah, I still   love   you.   Oh,   I see you

for - get   you.

Verse 2:

Now I know, that I had to borrow
And beg and steal and lie and cheat.
Just trying to keep you, just trying to please you,
'Cause being in love with you ain't cheap.
I pity the fool that falls in love with you, yeah,
(Oh, she's a gold digger, just thought you should know)
Ooh, I got some news for you, yeah,
I really hate your ass right now, yeah.

Chorus:

I see you driving 'round town...

Rolling In The Deep

Words & Music by Adele Adkins & Paul Epworth

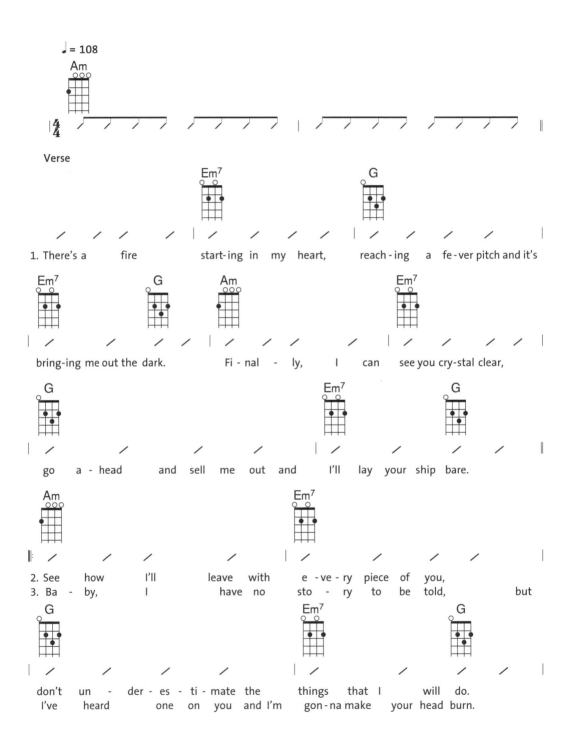

Verse

1. There's a fire start-ing in my heart, reach-ing a fe-ver pitch and it's bring-ing me out the dark. Fi - nal - ly, I can see you cry-stal clear,

go a - head and sell me out and I'll lay your ship bare.

2. See how I'll leave with e - ve - ry piece of you,
3. Ba - by, I have no sto - ry to be told, but

don't un - der - es - ti - mate the things that I will do.
I've heard one on you and I'm gon-na make your head burn.

Am / / / / | Em⁷ / / / / |

There's a fire start - ing in my heart,
Think of me in the depths of your des - pair,

G / / / / | Em⁷ / / / G / / ‖

reach - ing a fe - ver pitch and it's bring-ing me out the dark.
mak - ing home down there as mine sure won't be shared.

Bridge

F / / / / | G / / / | Em / / / / |

The scars of your love re-mind me of us, they keep me

F / / / / | / / / / | G / / / / |

think-ing that we al-most had it all. The scars of your love, they leave me

Em / / / / | E⁷ / / / / ‖

breath - less, I can't help feel - ing we could have had it

Chorus

Am / / / / | G / / / / | F / / / / |

all, roll - ing in the deep.

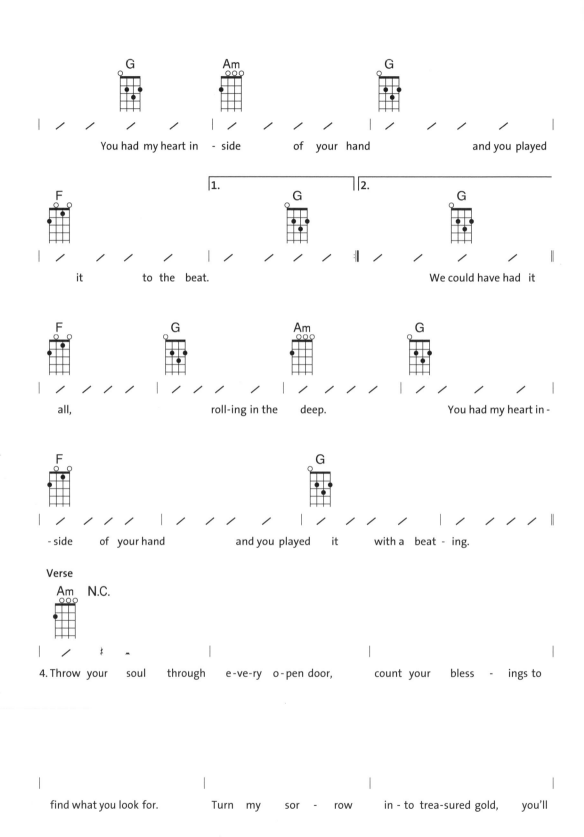

You had my heart in - side of your hand and you played

1.
it to the beat.

2.
We could have had it

all, roll-ing in the deep. You had my heart in -

- side of your hand and you played it with a beat - ing.

Verse

Am N.C.

4. Throw your soul through e-ve-ry o-pen door, count your bless - ings to

find what you look for. Turn my sor - row in - to trea-sured gold, you'll

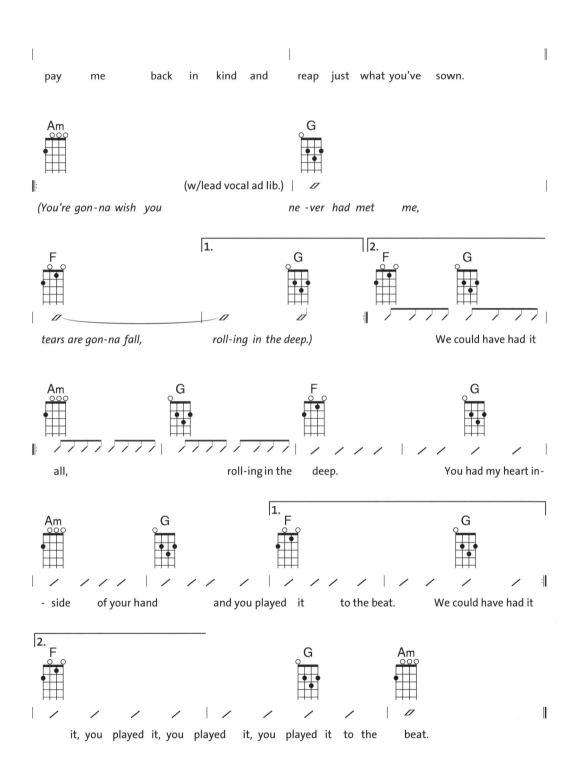

pay   me   back   in   kind and   reap just what you've sown.

Am   G

(w/lead vocal ad lib.)

(You're gon-na wish you   ne -ver had met   me,

F   1.   G   2. F   G

tears are gon-na fall,   roll-ing in the deep.)   We could have had it

Am   G   F   G

all,   roll-ing in the   deep.   You had my heart in-

Am   G   1. F   G

- side   of your hand   and you played it   to the beat.   We could have had it

2. F   G   Am

it, you played it, you played it, you played it to the   beat.

Hey Soul Sister

Words & Music by Espen Lind, Patrick Monahan & Amund Bjørklund

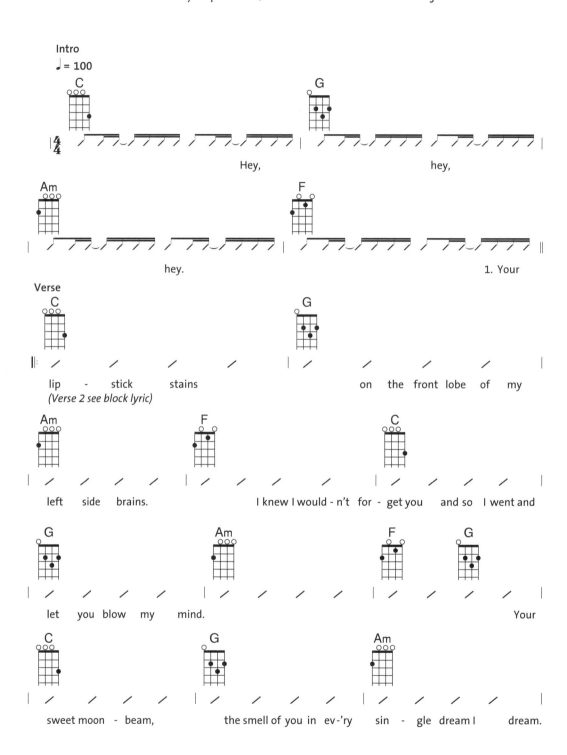

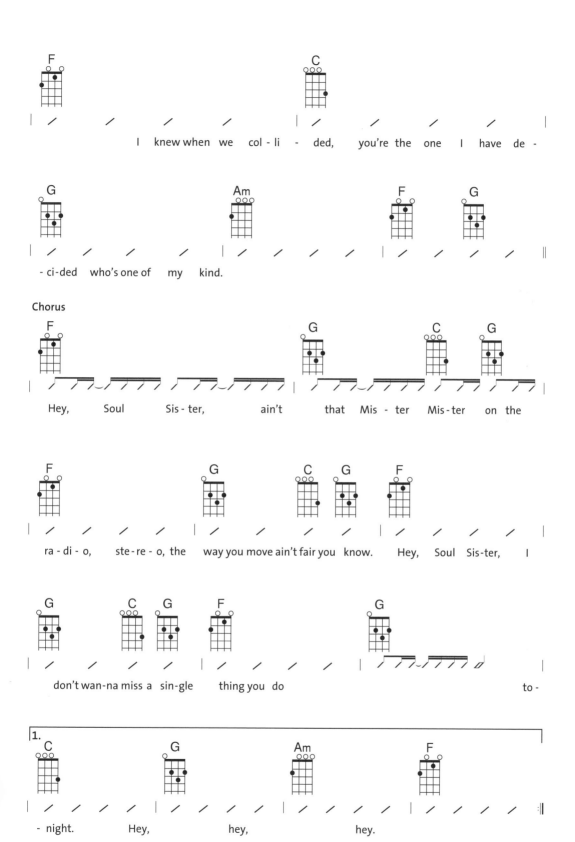

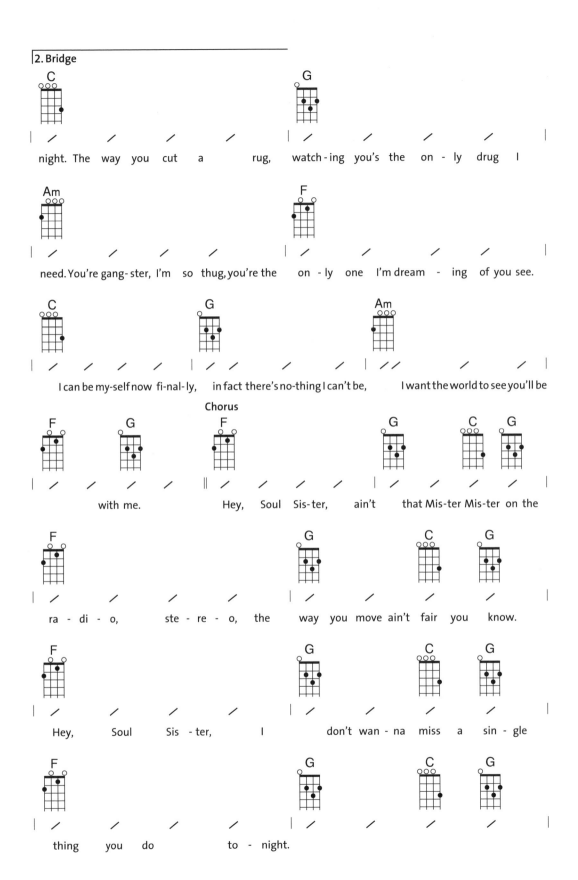

2. Bridge

C   G

| / / / / | / / / / |
night. The way you cut a   rug, watch-ing you's the on - ly drug I

Am   F

| / / / / | / / / / |
need. You're gang-ster, I'm so thug, you're the on - ly one I'm dream - ing of you see.

C   G   Am

| / / / / | / / / | / / / / |
I can be my-self now fi-nal-ly, in fact there's no-thing I can't be, I want the world to see you'll be

Chorus

F   G   F   G   C   G

| / / / / ‖ / / / / | / / / / |
with me. Hey, Soul Sis-ter, ain't that Mis-ter Mis-ter on the

F   G   C   G

| / / / / | / / / / |
ra - di - o, ste - re - o, the way you move ain't fair you know.

F   G   C   G

| / / / / | / / / / |
Hey, Soul Sis - ter, I don't wan - na miss a sin - gle

F   G   C   G

| / / / / | / / / / |
thing you do to - night.

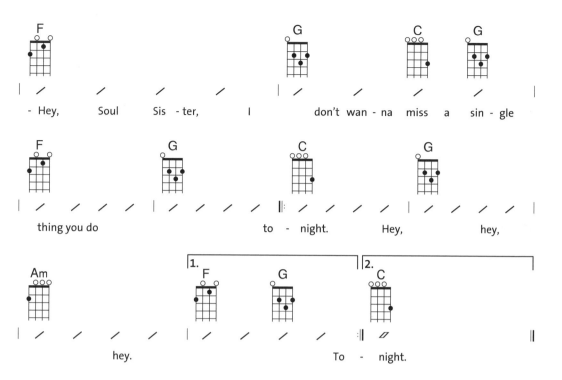

F				G		C	G
- Hey,	Soul	Sis - ter,	I		don't wan - na	miss a	sin - gle

F		G		C			G
thing you do				to - night.		Hey,	hey,

Am			1. F	G	2. C
hey.				To - night.

Verse 2:
Just in time,
I'm so glad you have a one-track mind like me.
You gave my life direction,
A game show love connection, we can't deny.
I'm so obsessed,
My heart is bound to beat right out my untrimmed chest.
'Cause I believe in you,
Like a virgin you're Madonna
And I'm always gonna wanna blow your mind.

Chorus:
Hey, Soul Sister,...

Just Wanna Play (My Ukulele)

Words & Music by Nick Patrick, Jeff Chegwin & Toby Chapman

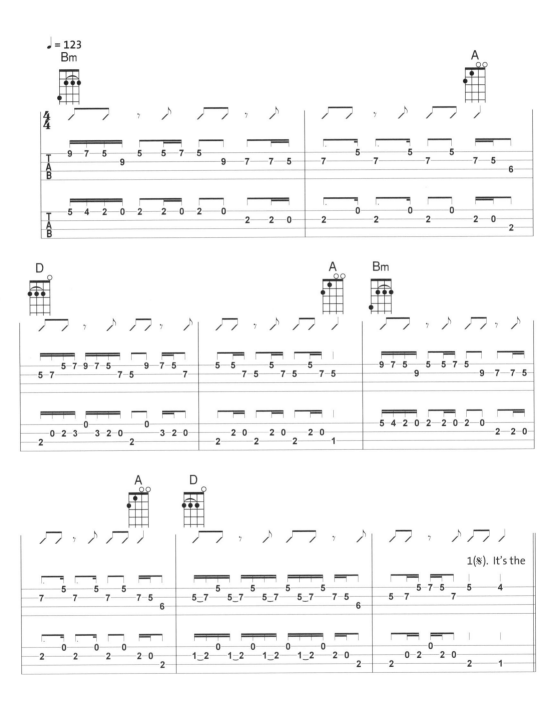

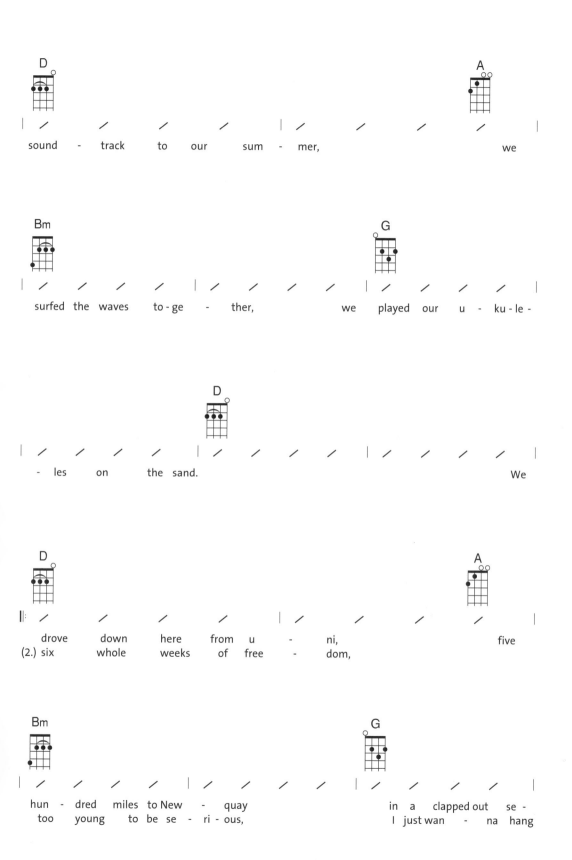

sound - track to our sum - mer, we
surfed the waves to - ge - ther, we played our u - ku - le -
- les on the sand. We
drove down here from u - ni, five
(2.) six whole weeks of free - dom,
hun - dred miles to New - quay in a clapped out se -
too young to be se - ri - ous, I just wan - na hang

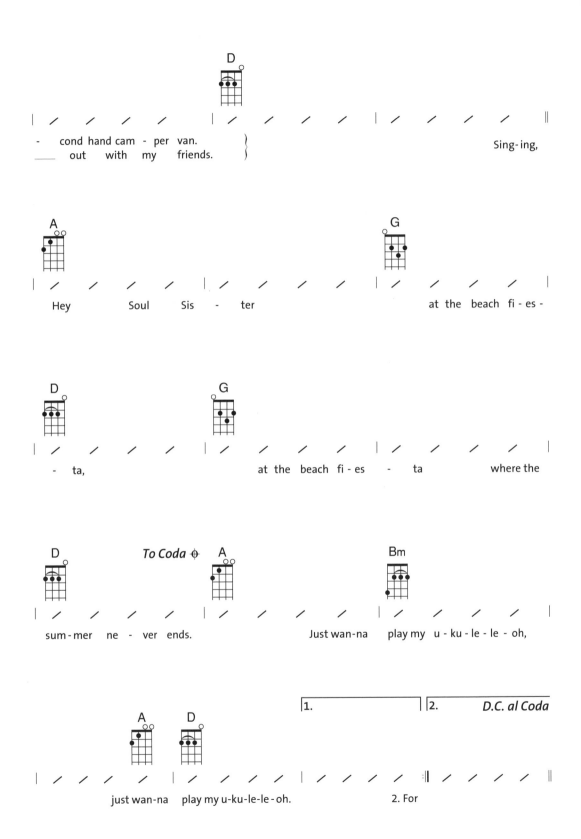

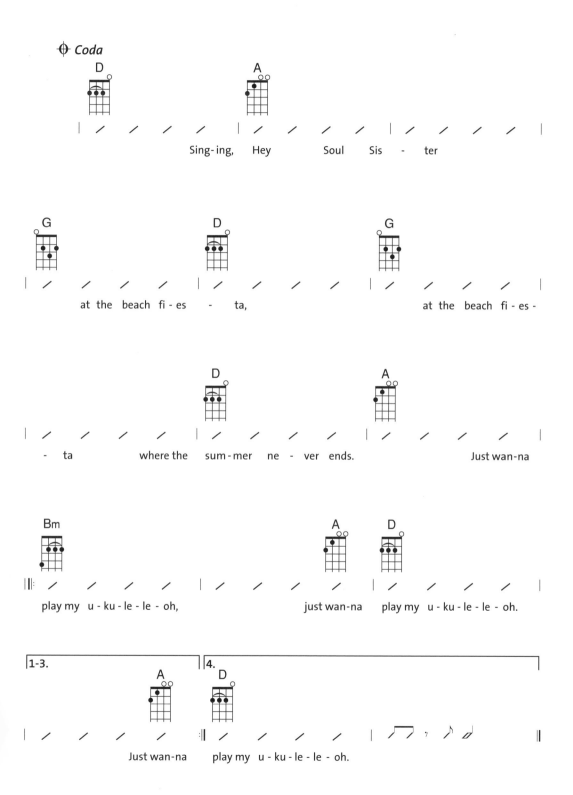

The A Team

Words & Music by Ed Sheeran

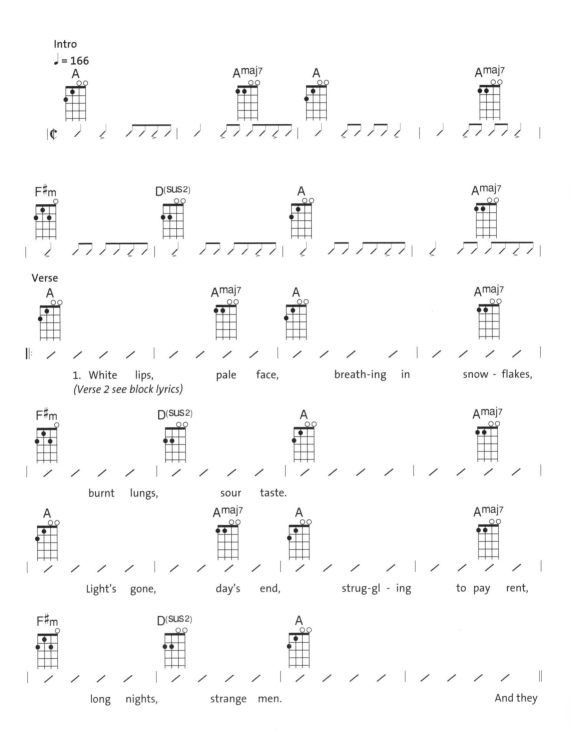

1. White lips, pale face, breath-ing in snow - flakes,

(Verse 2 see block lyrics)

burnt lungs, sour taste.

Light's gone, day's end, strug-gl - ing to pay rent,

long nights, strange men. And they

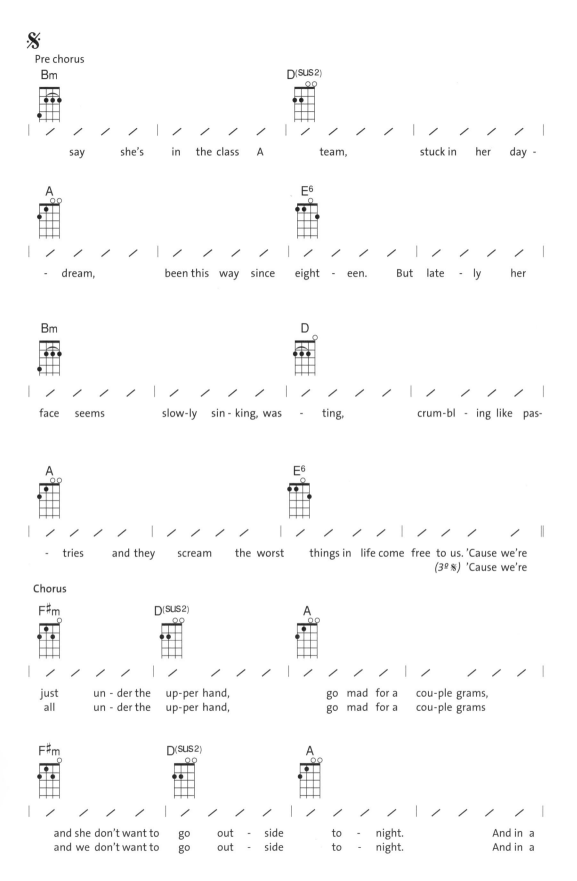

Pre chorus

Bm

D(sus2)

| ╱ ╱ ╱ ╱ | ╱ ╱ ╱ ╱ | ╱ ╱ ╱ ╱ | ╱ ╱ ╱ ╱ |

say   she's   in   the class   A   team,   stuck in   her   day -

A

E6

| ╱ ╱ ╱ ╱ | ╱ ╱ ╱ ╱ | ╱ ╱ ╱ ╱ | ╱ ╱ ╱ ╱ |

- dream,   been this way since   eight - een.   But   late - ly   her

Bm

D

| ╱ ╱ ╱ ╱ | ╱ ╱ ╱ ╱ | ╱ ╱ ╱ ╱ | ╱ ╱ ╱ ╱ |

face   seems   slow-ly sin - king, was   -   ting,   crum-bl - ing like pas-

A

E6

| ╱ ╱ ╱ ╱ | ╱ ╱ ╱ ╱ | ╱ ╱ ╱ ╱ | ╱ ╱ ╱ ╱ ‖

- tries   and they   scream   the worst   things in life come free to us. 'Cause we're
                                                              (3º 𝄋) 'Cause we're

Chorus

F#m

D(sus2)

A

| ╱ ╱ ╱ ╱ | ╱ ╱ ╱ ╱ | ╱ ╱ ╱ ╱ | ╱ ╱ ╱ ╱ |

just   un - der the   up-per hand,   go mad for a   cou-ple grams,
all   un - der the   up-per hand,   go mad for a   cou-ple grams

F#m

D(sus2)

A

| ╱ ╱ ╱ ╱ | ╱ ╱ ╱ ╱ | ╱ ╱ ╱ ╱ | ╱ ╱ ╱ ╱ |

and she don't want to   go   out - side   to - night.   And in a
and we don't want to   go   out - side   to - night.   And in a

25

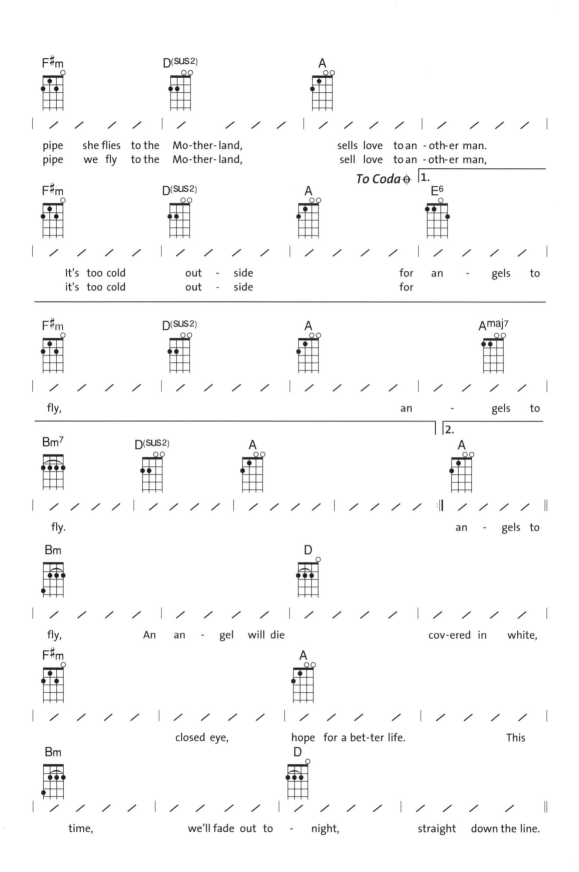

F#m   D(sus2)   A

pipe   she flies   to the   Mo-ther-land,   sells love   to an -oth-er man.
pipe   we fly   to the   Mo-ther-land,   sell love   to an -oth-er man,

To Coda ⊕ |1.

F#m   D(sus2)   A   E6

It's too cold   out - side   for   an - gels   to
it's too cold   out - side   for

F#m   D(sus2)   A   Amaj7

fly,   an - gels   to

|2.

Bm7   D(sus2)   A   A

fly.   an - gels   to

Bm   D

fly,   An   an - gel   will die   cov-ered in   white,

F#m   A

closed eye,   hope for a bet-ter life.   This

Bm   D

time,   we'll fade out to - night,   straight   down the line.

26

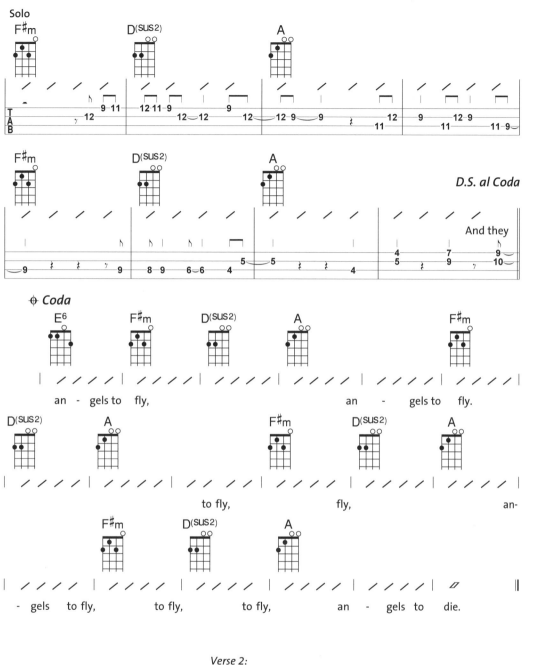

Verse 2:
Ripped gloves, raincoat,
Tried to swim and stay afloat
Dry house, wet clothes.
Loose change, bank notes,
Weary-eyed, dry throat,
Call girl, no phone.

Pre chorus 2:
And they say....

Chorus 2:
'Cause we're just...

Price Tag

Words & Music by Lukasz Gottwald, Claude Kelly, Bobby Ray Simmons & Jessica Cornish

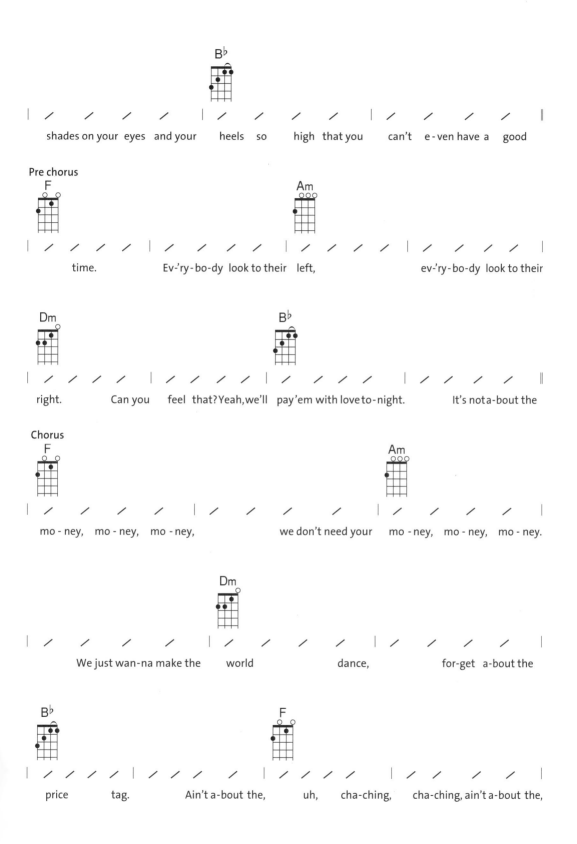

Bb

shades on your eyes and your heels so high that you can't e-ven have a good

Pre chorus

F   **Am**

time.   Ev-'ry-bo-dy look to their left,   ev-'ry-bo-dy look to their

Dm   **Bb**

right.   Can you feel that? Yeah, we'll pay 'em with love to-night.   It's not a-bout the

Chorus

F   **Am**

mo-ney, mo-ney, mo-ney,   we don't need your mo-ney, mo-ney, mo-ney.

Dm

We just wan-na make the world   dance,   for-get a-bout the

Bb   **F**

price   tag.   Ain't a-bout the, uh, cha-ching, cha-ching, ain't a-bout the,

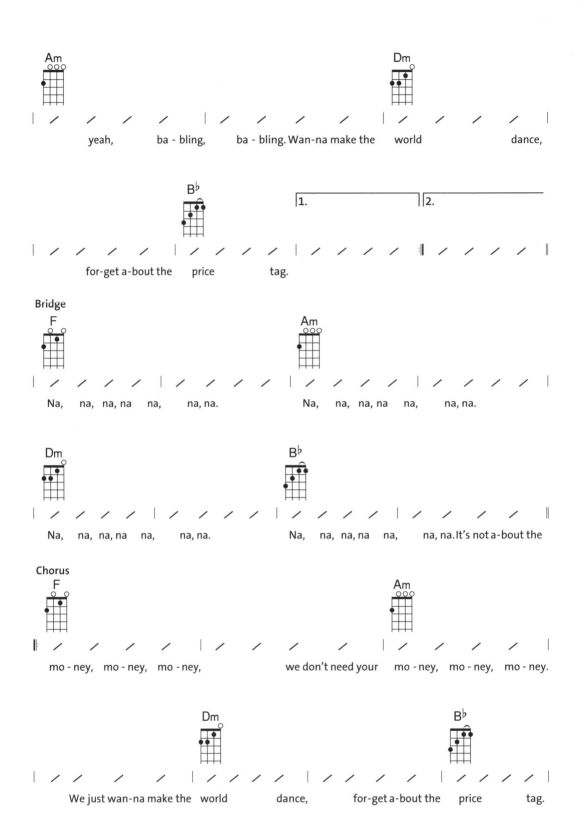

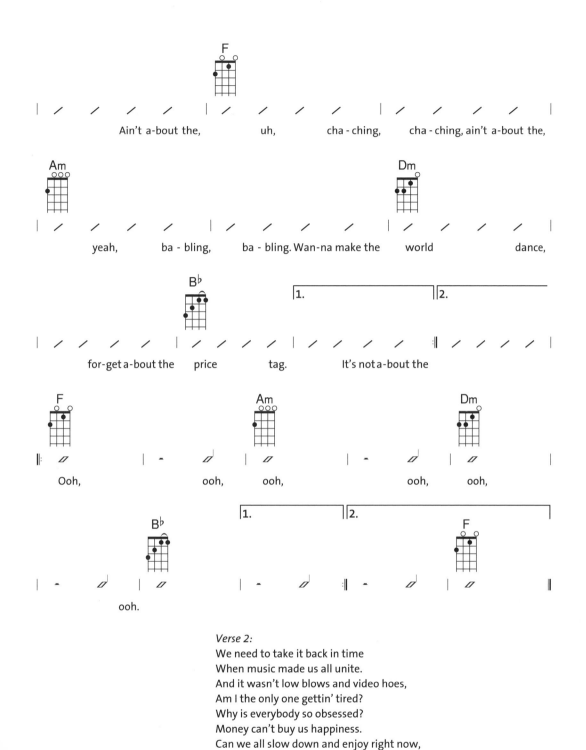

F

| / | / | / | / | | / | / | / | / | | / | / | / | / |

Ain't a-bout the,   uh,   cha - ching,   cha - ching, ain't a-bout the,

Am   **Dm**

| / | / | / | / | | / | / | / | / | | / | / | / | / |

yeah,   ba - bling,   ba - bling. Wan-na make the   world   dance,

B♭ |1. |2.

| / | / | / | / | | / | / | / | / | | / | / | / | / | : | / | / | / | / |

for-get a-bout the   price   tag.   It's not a-bout the

F   **Am**   **Dm**

‖: // | - // | // | - // | // |

Ooh,   ooh,   ooh,   ooh,   ooh,

           |1. |2.

B♭   **F**

| - // | // | | - // : - // | // | ‖

ooh.

Verse 2:
We need to take it back in time
When music made us all unite.
And it wasn't low blows and video hoes,
Am I the only one gettin' tired?
Why is everybody so obsessed?
Money can't buy us happiness.
Can we all slow down and enjoy right now,
Guarantee we'll be feelin' all right.

Pre chorus:
Everybody look to their left...

The Cave

Words & Music by Mumford & Sons

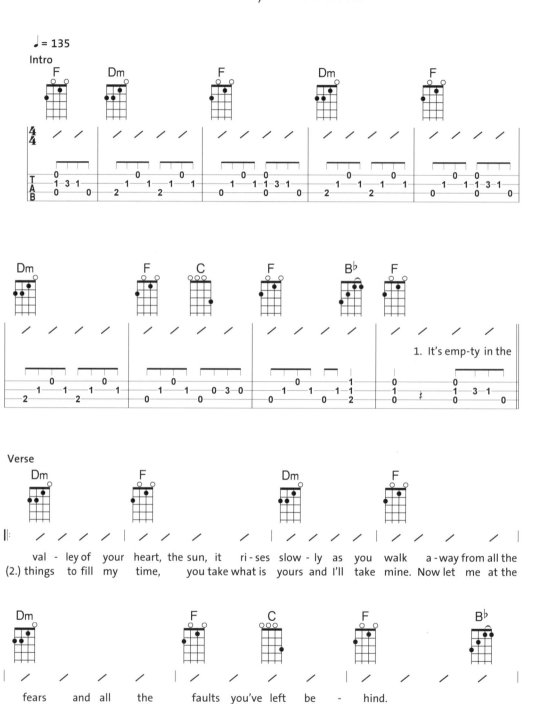

val - ley of your heart, the sun, it ri - ses slow - ly as you walk a - way from all the
(2.) things to fill my time, you take what is yours and I'll take mine. Now let me at the

fears and all the faults you've left be - hind.
truth which will re - fresh my bro - ken mind.

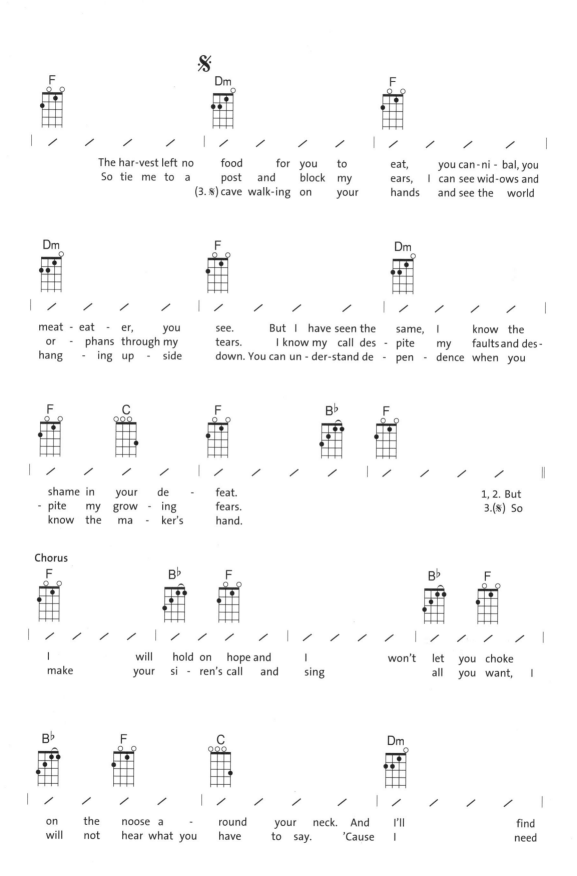

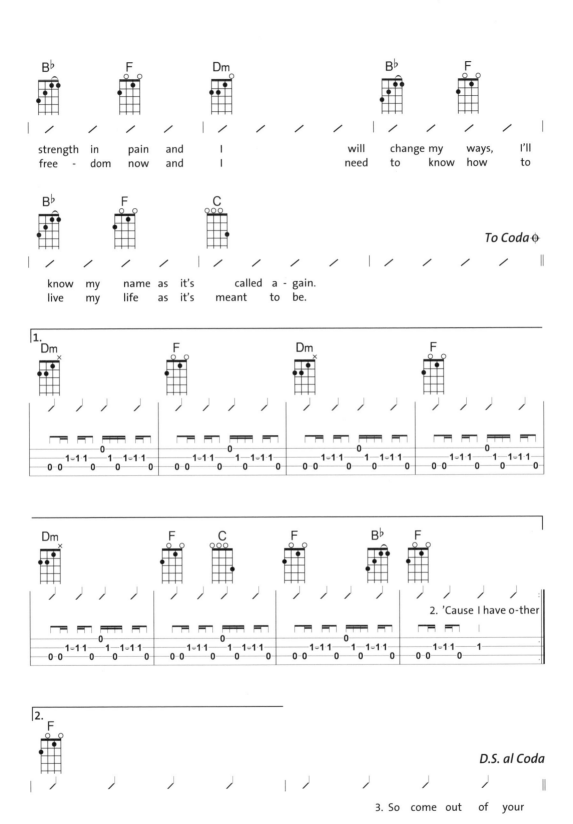

strength in pain and I
free - dom now and I

will change my ways, I'll
need to know how to

know my name as it's called a - gain.
live my life as it's meant to be.

To Coda

1.

2. 'Cause I have o-ther

2.

D.S. al Coda

3. So come out of your

34

Sky

Words & Music by Logan Wilson

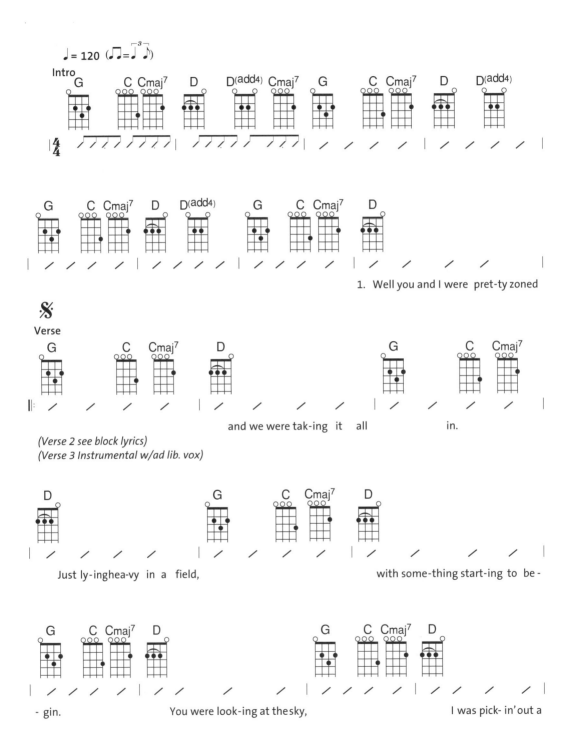

1. Well you and I were pret-ty zoned

and we were tak-ing it all in.

(Verse 2 see block lyrics)
(Verse 3 Instrumental w/ad lib. vox)

Just ly-ing hea-vy in a field, with some-thing start-ing to be -

- gin. You were look-ing at the sky, I was pick- in' out a

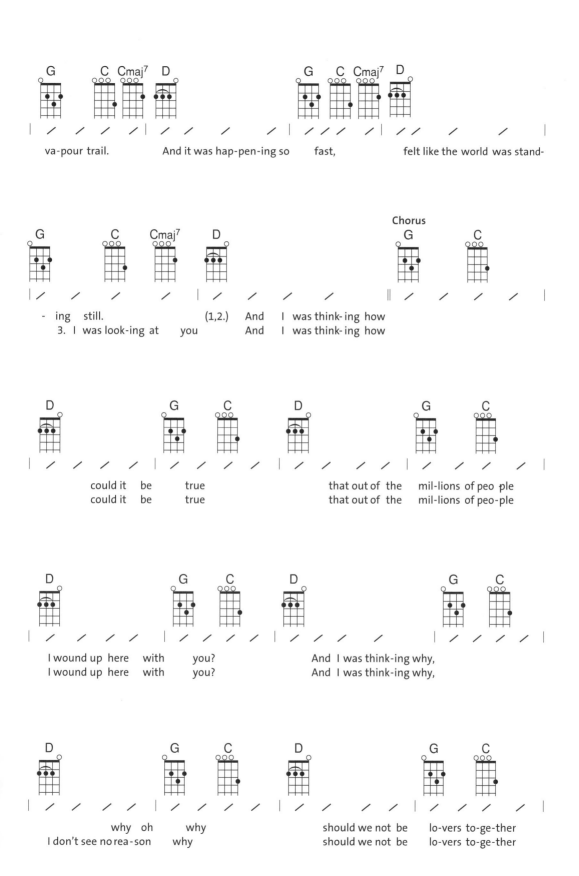

va-pour trail.   And it was hap-pen-ing so   fast,   felt like the world was stand-

- ing still.   (1,2.) And   I was think- ing how
    3. I was look-ing at   you   And   I was think- ing how

Chorus

could it be   true   that out of the   mil-lions of peo ple
could it be   true   that out of the   mil-lions of peo-ple

I wound up here with   you?   And I was think-ing why,
I wound up here with   you?   And I was think-ing why,

        why oh   why   should we not be   lo-vers to-ge-ther
I don't see no rea-son why   should we not be   lo-vers to-ge-ther

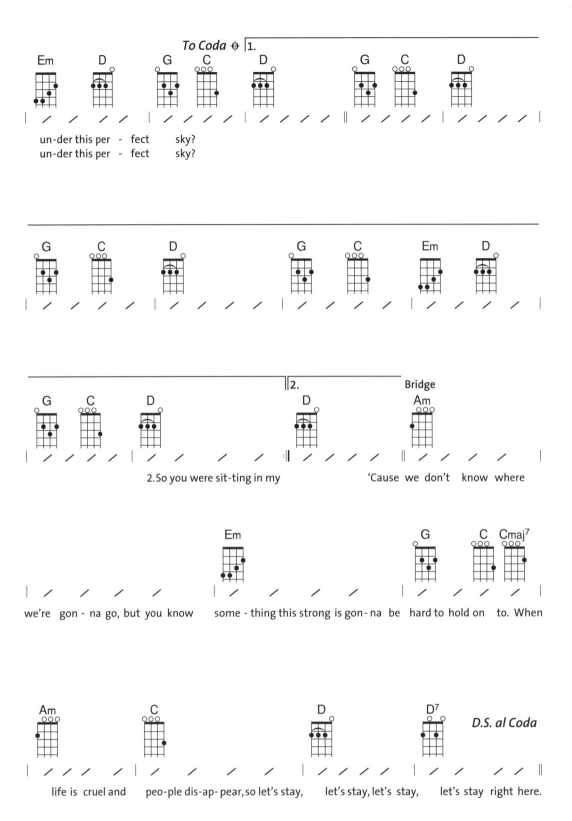

To Coda ⊕ |1.

Em   D   G   C   D   G   C   D

un-der this per - fect   sky?
un-der this per - fect   sky?

G   C   D   G   C   Em   D

G   C   D ||2.   D   Bridge
Am

2.So you were sit-ting in my   'Cause we don't know where

Em   G   C   Cmaj⁷

we're gon - na go, but you know   some - thing this strong is gon-na be hard to hold on to. When

Am   C   D   D⁷   *D.S. al Coda*

life is cruel and   peo-ple dis-ap-pear, so let's stay,   let's stay, let's stay,   let's stay right here.

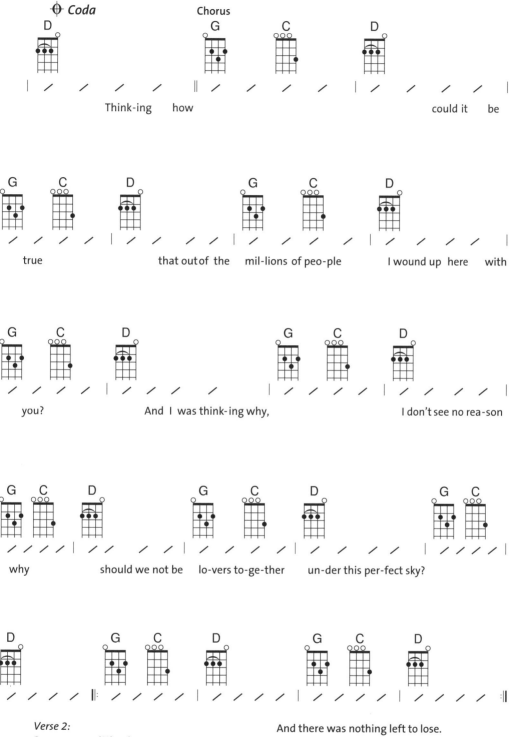

⊕ Coda

Chorus

Think-ing how ..... could it be

true ..... that out of the mil-lions of peo-ple ..... I wound up here with

you? ..... And I was think-ing why, ... I don't see no rea-son

why ..... should we not be lo-vers to-ge-ther un-der this per-fect sky?

Verse 2:
So you were sitting in my car
And we were high up on a hill.
Though the wind was blowing hard,
We didn't care, we both had time to kill.
And everything we said was true

And there was nothing left to lose.
All wrapped up in your camp college coat
And those rainbow coloured laces in your shoes.

Chorus:
And I was thinking...

Over The Rainbow

Words by E.Y. Harburg
Music by Harold Arlen

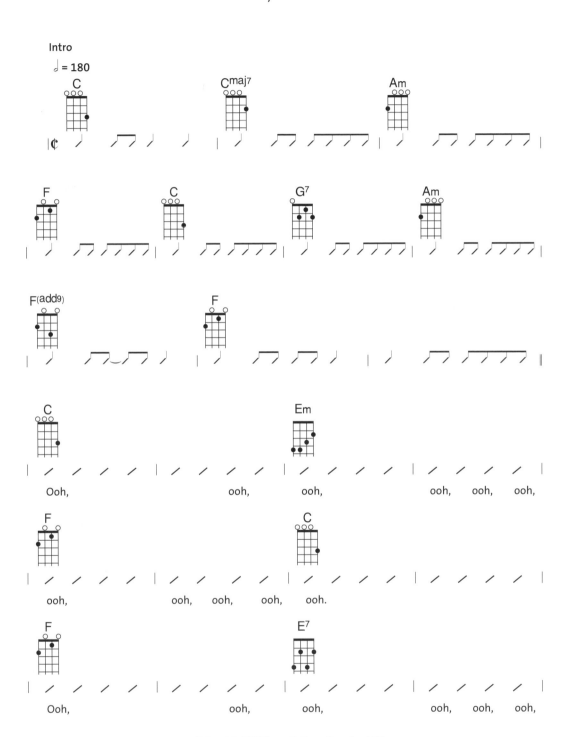

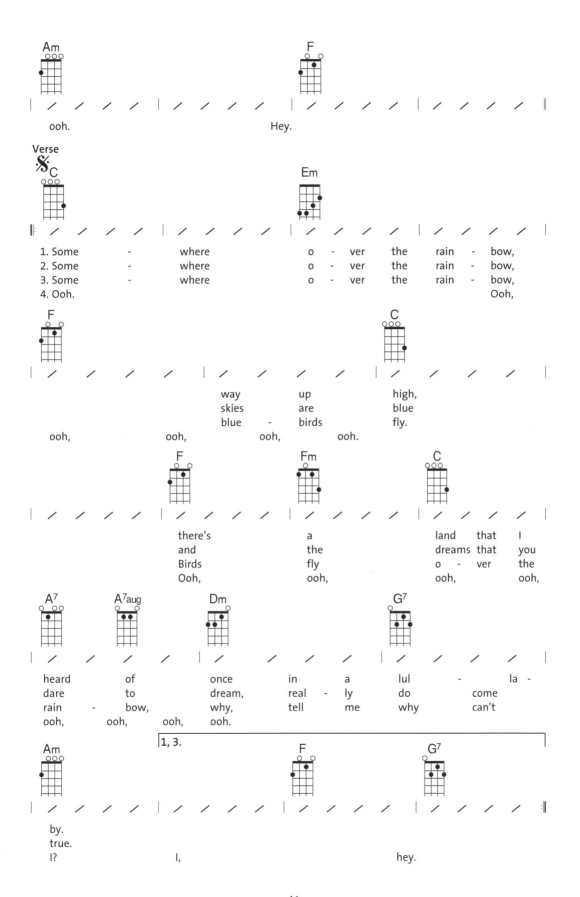

Am   F

| / / / / | / / / / | / / / / | / / / / ||

ooh.   Hey.

Verse

C   Em

||: / / / / | / / / / | / / / / | / / / / |

1. Some   where   o - ver   the   rain - bow,
2. Some   where   o - ver   the   rain - bow,
3. Some   where   o - ver   the   rain - bow,
4. Ooh.   Ooh,

F   C

| / / / / | / / / / | / / / / |

          way   up   high,
          skies   are   blue
          blue - birds   fly.
ooh,   ooh,   ooh,   ooh.

F   Fm   C

| / / / / | / / / / | / / / / |

      there's   a   land   that   I
      and   the   dreams that   you
      Birds   fly   o - ver   the
      Ooh,   ooh,   ooh,   ooh,

A⁷   A⁷aug   Dm   G⁷

| / / / / | / / / / | / / / / |

heard   of   once   in   a   lul - la -
dare   to   dream,   real - ly   do   come
rain - bow,   why,   tell   me   why   can't
ooh,   ooh,   ooh,   ooh.

1, 3.

Am   F   G⁷

| / / / / | / / / / | / / / / | / / / / :||

by.
true.
I?   I,   hey.

41

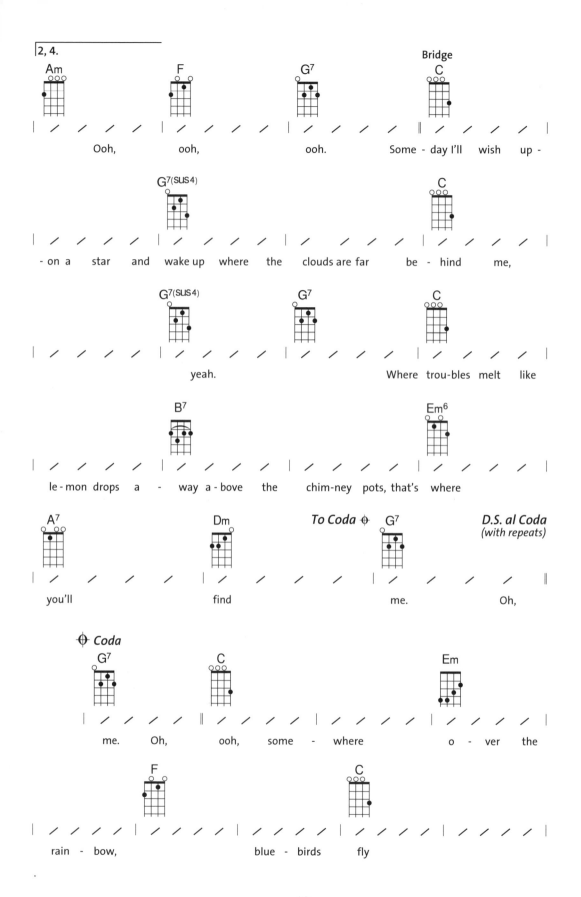

Birds ... fly ... o - ver the rain - bow,

why, oh why can't I? I

Outro

hey yeah. *(Vocal ad lib.)*

To fade

43

5 Years Time

Words & Music by Charlie Fink

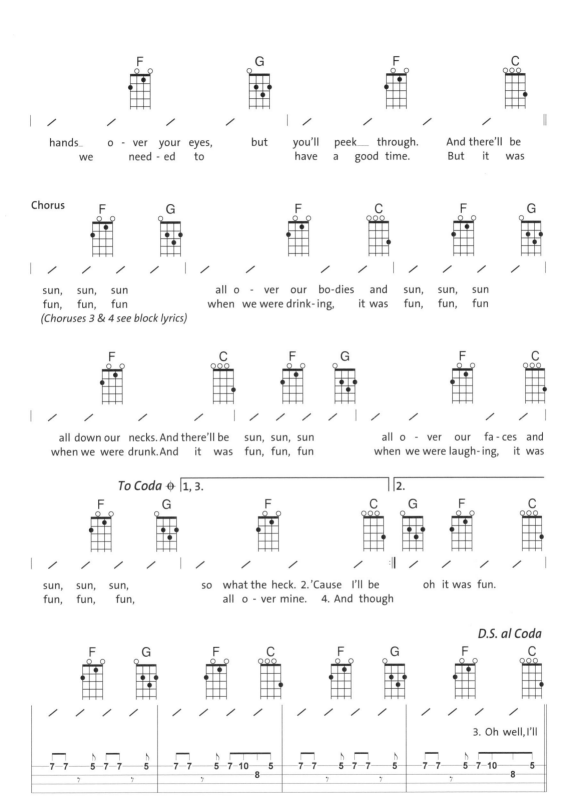

Verse 3:
Oh well, I'll look at you and say, "it's the happiest that I've ever been."
And I'll say, "I no longer feel I have to be James Dean."
And she'll say, "Yeah well, I feel all pretty happy too
And I'm always pretty happy when I'm just kicking back with you."

Chorus 3:
And it'll be love, love, love all through our bodies,
And love, love, love all through our minds.
And it'll be love, love, love all over her face,
And love, love, love all over mine.

Verse 4:
And though nearly all these moments are just in my head,
I'll be thinking about them as I'm lying in bed.
And I know that it really, it might, not even come true,
But in my mind I'm having a pretty good time with you.

Chorus 4:
Oh, in five years time I might not know you,
In five years time we might not speak.
Oh, in five years time we might not get along,
In five years time you might just prove me wrong.

Chorus 5:
Oh, there'll be...

Through It All

Words & Music by Nicky Campbell

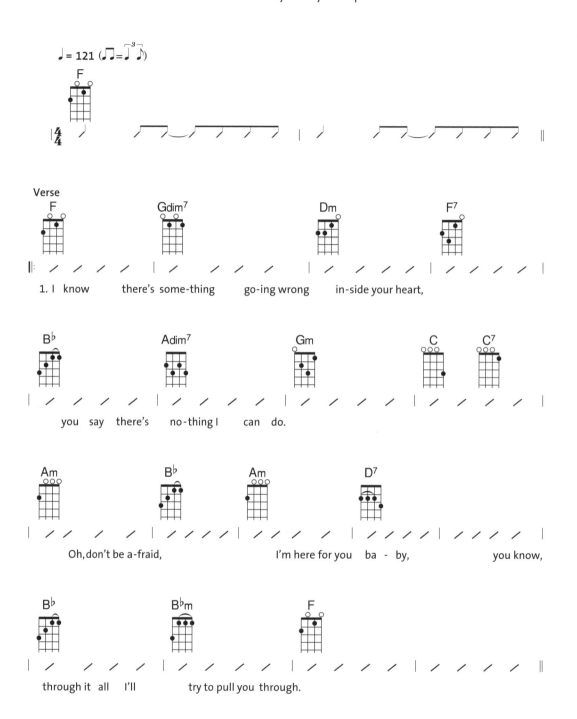

♩ = 121

F

Verse

F   Gdim⁷   Dm   F⁷

1. I know there's some-thing go-ing wrong in-side your heart,

B♭   Adim⁷   Gm   C   C⁷

you say there's no-thing I can do.

Am   B♭   Am   D⁷

Oh, don't be a-fraid, I'm here for you ba - by, you know,

B♭   B♭m   F

through it all I'll try to pull you through.

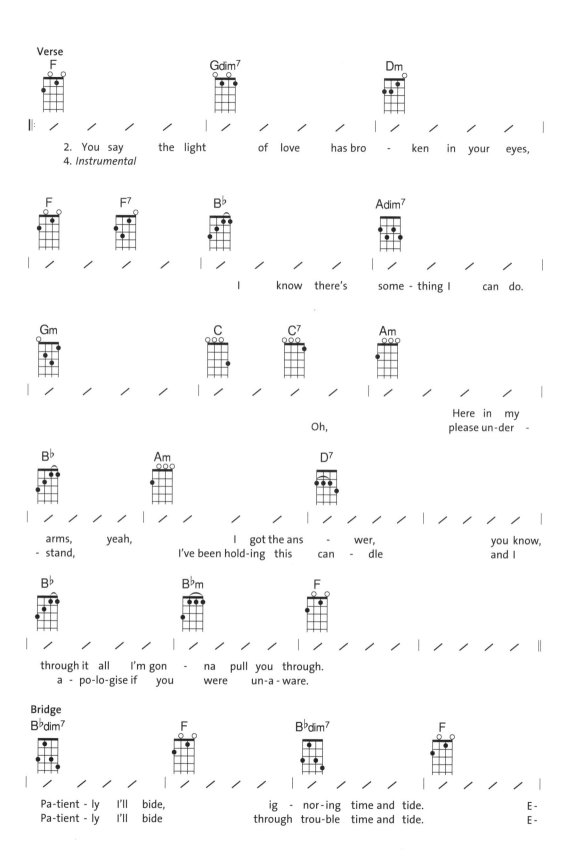

Verse

F   Gdim⁷   Dm

2. You say   the light   of love   has bro - ken   in   your   eyes,
4. *Instrumental*

F   F⁷   B♭   Adim⁷

I   know   there's   some - thing I   can   do.

Gm   C   C⁷   Am

                                     Here in   my
                        Oh,   please un-der -

B♭   Am   D⁷

arms,   yeah,   I   got the ans - wer,   you know,
- stand,   I've been hold-ing this   can - dle   and I

B♭   B♭m   F

through it all   I'm gon - na   pull you through.
a - po-lo-gise if   you   were   un-a - ware.

Bridge

B♭dim⁷   F   B♭dim⁷   F

Pa-tient - ly   I'll   bide,   ig - nor-ing time and tide.   E -
Pa-tient - ly   I'll   bide   through trou-ble time and tide.   E -

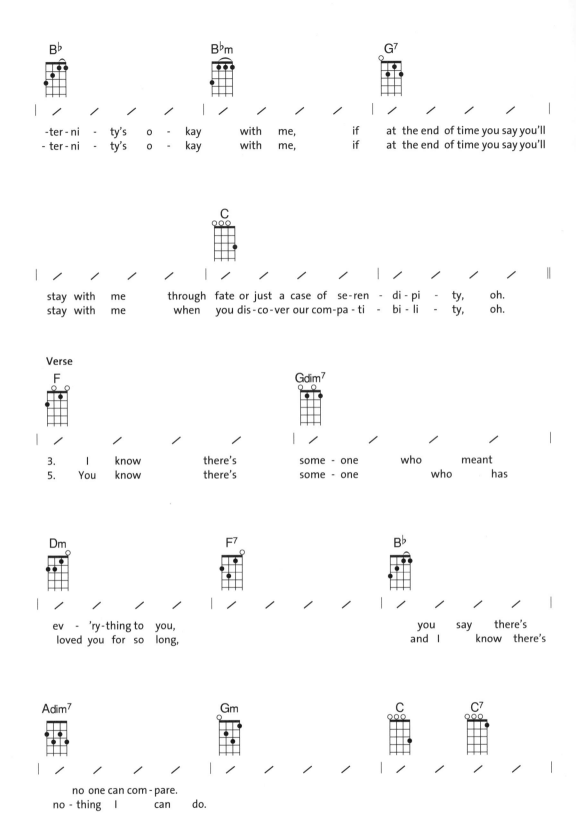

B♭

B♭m

G⁷

| / | / | / | / | | / | / | / | / | | / | / | / | / | |

-ter-ni - ty's o - kay   with   me,   if   at the end of time you say you'll
- ter-ni - ty's o - kay   with   me,   if   at the end of time you say you'll

C

| / | / | / | / | | / | / | / | / | | / | / | / | / | ||

stay with   me   through fate or just a case of se-ren - di - pi - ty,   oh.
stay with   me   when you dis-co-ver our com-pa-ti - bi-li - ty,   oh.

Verse

F

Gdim⁷

| / | / | / | / | | / | / | / | / | |

3.   I   know   there's   some - one   who   meant
5.   You know   there's   some - one   who   has

Dm

F⁷

B♭

| / | / | / | / | | / | / | / | / | | / | / | / | / | |

ev - 'ry-thing to you,   you   say   there's
loved you for so long,   and I   know there's

Adim⁷

Gm

C

C⁷

| / | / | / | / | | / | / | / | / | | / | / | / | / | |

     no one can com - pare.
     no - thing I   can   do.

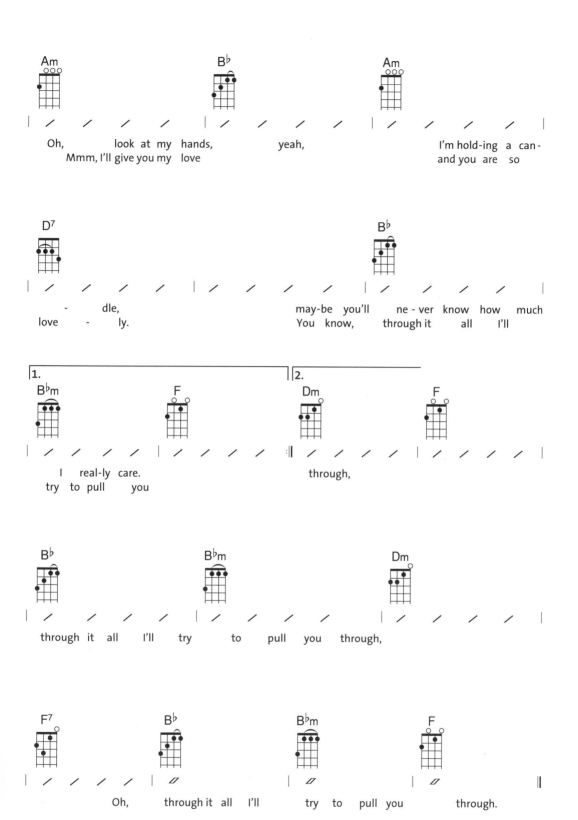

Am | Bb | Am
/ / / / | / / / / | / / / /

Oh,   look at my hands,   yeah,   I'm hold-ing a can-
Mmm, I'll give you my love   and you are so

D7 | | Bb
/ / / / | / / / / | / / / /

      -    dle,   may-be you'll   ne - ver know how   much
love -   ly.   You know,   through it   all   I'll

1.
Bbm | F | : 2. Dm | F
/ / / / | / / / / : | / / / / | / / / /

    I   real-ly care.   through,
try to pull   you

Bb | Bbm | Dm
/ / / / | / / / / | / / / /

through it all   I'll   try   to   pull you through,

F7 | Bb | Bbm | F
/ / / / | // | // | // ||

         Oh,   through it all I'll   try to pull you   through.

51

I'm Yours

Words & Music by Jason Mraz

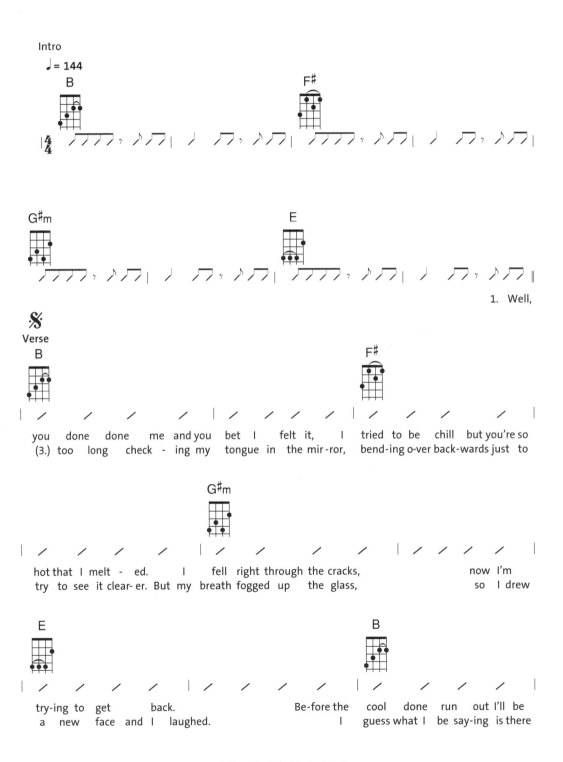

Intro

♩ = 144

1. Well,

Verse

you done done me and you bet I felt it, I tried to be chill but you're so
(3.) too long check-ing my tongue in the mir-ror, bend-ing o-ver back-wards just to

hot that I melt-ed. I fell right through the cracks, now I'm
try to see it clear-er. But my breath fogged up the glass, so I drew

try-ing to get back. Be-fore the cool done run out I'll be
a new face and I laughed. I guess what I be say-ing is there

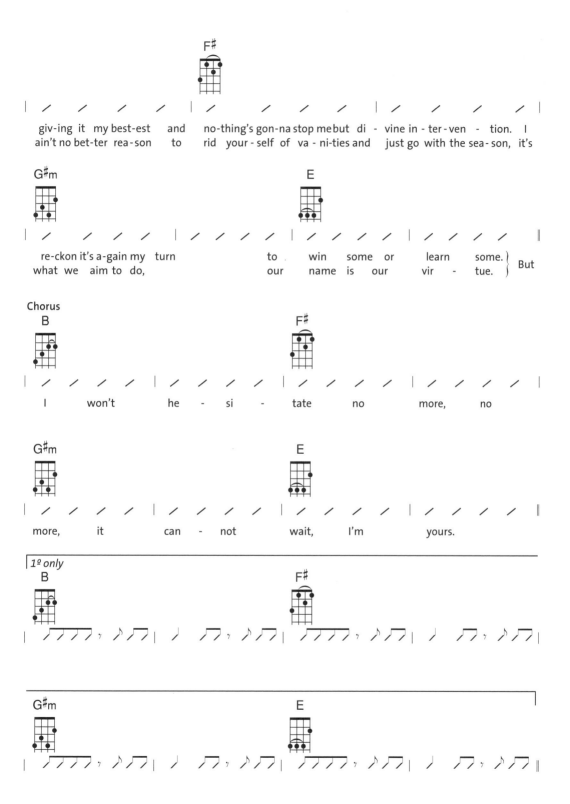

F#

giv-ing it my best-est and no-thing's gon-na stop me but di - vine in - ter - ven - tion. I
ain't no bet-ter rea-son to rid your-self of va - ni-ties and just go with the sea-son, it's

G#m   **E**

re-ckon it's a-gain my turn   to win some or learn some. ⎫
what we aim to do,   our name is our vir - tue. ⎭ But

Chorus
B   **F#**

I won't he - si - tate no more, no

G#m   **E**

more, it can - not wait, I'm yours.

1º only
B   **F#**

G#m   **E**

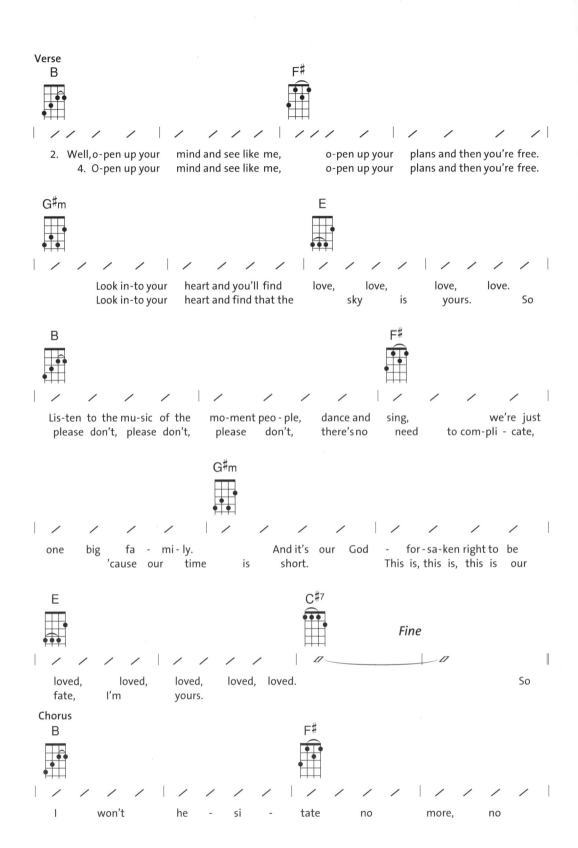

Verse

B   F#

| ╱ ╱ | ╱ | ╱ | | ╱ | ╱ | ╱ | ╱ | | ╱ ╱ | ╱ | | ╱ | ╱ | ╱ |

2. Well, o-pen up your   mind and see like me,   o-pen up your   plans and then you're free.
4. O-pen up your   mind and see like me,   o-pen up your   plans and then you're free.

G#m   E

Look in-to your   heart and you'll find   love,   love,   love,   love.
Look in-to your   heart and find that the   sky   is   yours.   So

B   F#

Lis-ten to the mu-sic of the   mo-ment peo-ple,   dance and   sing,   we're just
please don't, please don't,   please   don't,   there's no   need   to com-pli - cate,

G#m

one   big   fa - mi - ly.   And it's our   God - for - sa-ken right to be
'cause our   time   is   short.   This is, this is, this is   our

E   C#7   *Fine*

loved,   loved,   loved,   loved, loved.   So
fate,   I'm   yours.

Chorus

B   F#

I   won't   he - si - tate   no   more,   no

54

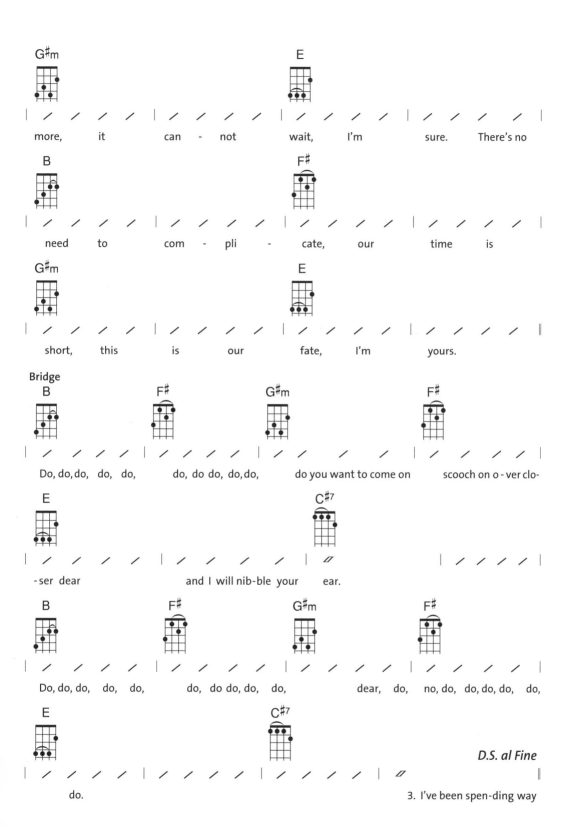

G#m   E

| / / / / | / / / / | / / / / | / / / / |

more,   it   can - not   wait,   I'm   sure.   There's no

B   F#

| / / / / | / / / / | / / / / | / / / / |

need   to   com - pli - cate,   our   time   is

G#m   E

| / / / / | / / / / | / / / / | / / / / ‖

short,   this   is   our   fate,   I'm   yours.

Bridge

B   F#   G#m   F#

| / / / / | / / / / | / / / / | / / / / |

Do, do, do,   do,   do,   do, do do, do, do,   do you want to come on   scooch on o - ver clo-

E   C#7

| / / / / | / / / / | 𝄚 | / / / / |

-ser dear   and I will nib-ble your   ear.

B   F#   G#m   F#

| / / / / | / / / / | / / / / | / / / / |

Do, do, do,   do,   do,   do, do do, do,   do,   dear,   do,   no, do, do, do, do,   do,

E   C#7

                                           D.S. al Fine

| / / / / | / / / / | / / / / | 𝄚   ‖

do.   3. I've been spen-ding way

You Make Me Happy

Words & Music by Ronald Harwood

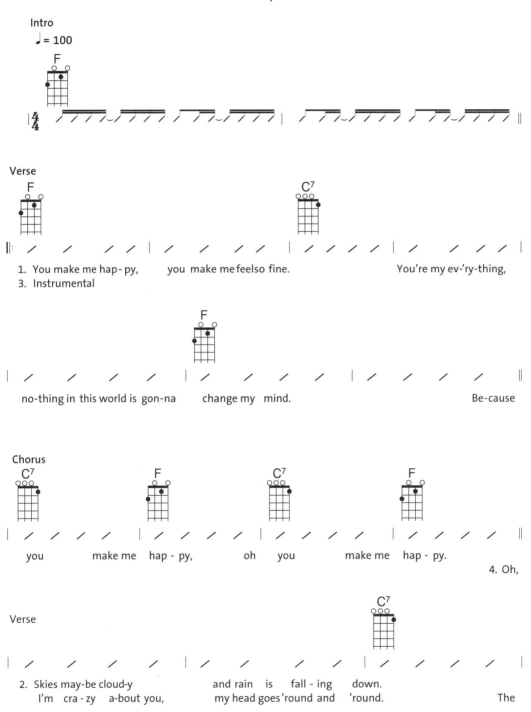

Intro

♩ = 100

F

Verse

F   C⁷

1. You make me hap-py,   you make me feel so fine.   You're my ev-'ry-thing,
3. Instrumental

F

no-thing in this world is gon-na   change my   mind.   Be-cause

Chorus

C⁷   F   C⁷   F

you   make me hap-py,   oh   you   make me   hap-py.

4. Oh,

Verse

C⁷

2. Skies may-be cloud-y   and rain is   fall-ing   down.
   I'm cra-zy a-bout you,   my head goes 'round and   'round.   The

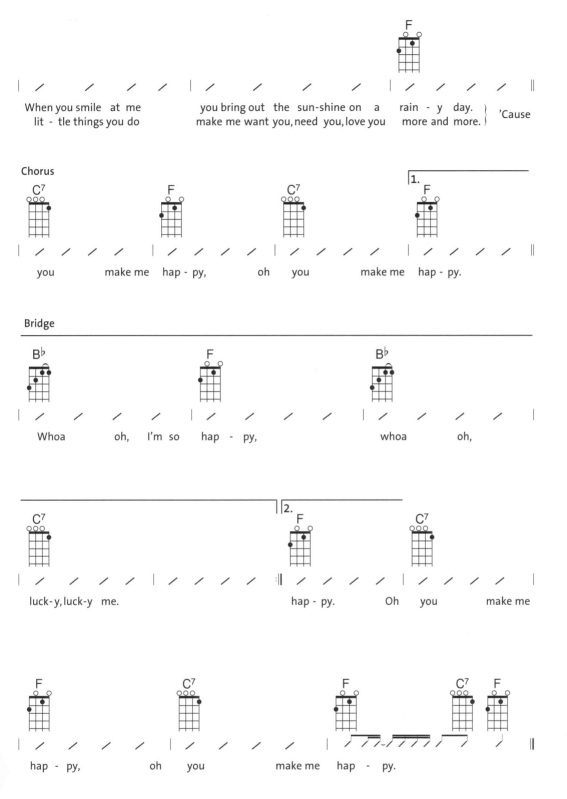

When you smile at me you bring out the sun-shine on a rain - y day.
lit - tle things you do make me want you, need you, love you more and more. 'Cause

Chorus

C7   F   C7   1. F

you make me hap - py, oh you make me hap - py.

Bridge

Bb   F   Bb

Whoa oh, I'm so hap - py, whoa oh,

C7   2. F   C7

luck-y, luck-y me. hap - py. Oh you make me

F   C7   F   C7   F

hap - py, oh you make me hap - py.

The Lazy Song

Words & Music by Ari Levine, Philip Lawrence, Peter Hernandez & Keinan Abdi Warsame

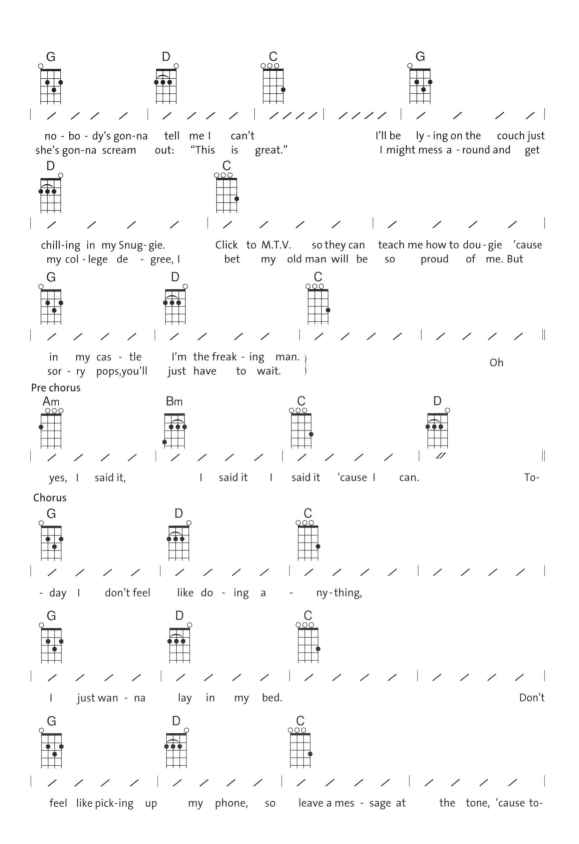

G   D   C   G

| / / / / | / / / | / / / / | / / / / | / / / / |

no - bo - dy's gon-na   tell   me I   can't   I'll be   ly - ing on the   couch just
she's gon-na scream   out: "This   is   great."   I might mess a - round and   get

D   C

| / / / / | / / / / | / / / / | / / / / |

chill-ing in my Snug-gie.   Click to M.T.V.   so they can   teach me how to dou-gie 'cause
my col-lege de - gree, I   bet   my old man will be   so   proud   of me. But

G   D   C

| / / / / | / / / / | / / / / | / / / / ‖

in   my cas - tle   I'm the freak - ing man. ⎫
sor - ry pops,you'll   just have   to wait. ⎭   Oh

Pre chorus

Am   Bm   C   D

| / / / / | / / / / | / / / / | ⫽ | ‖

yes, I   said it,   I   said it   I   said it 'cause I   can.   To-

Chorus

G   D   C

| / / / / | / / / / | / / / / | / / / / | / / / / |

- day I   don't feel   like do - ing a   -   ny-thing,

G   D   C

| / / / / | / / / / | / / / / | / / / / | / / / / |

I   just wan - na   lay   in   my   bed.   Don't

G   D   C

| / / / / | / / / / | / / / / | / / / / |

feel like pick-ing   up   my   phone,   so   leave a mes - sage at   the   tone, 'cause to-

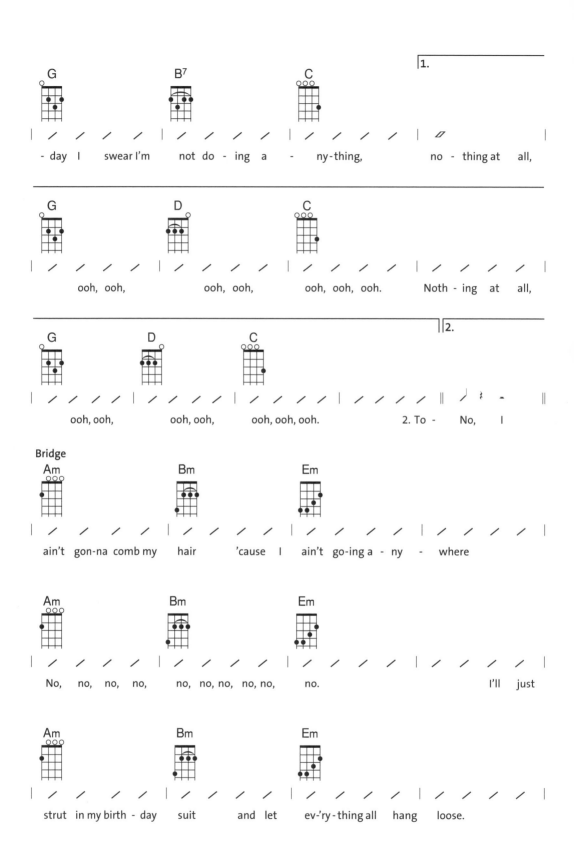

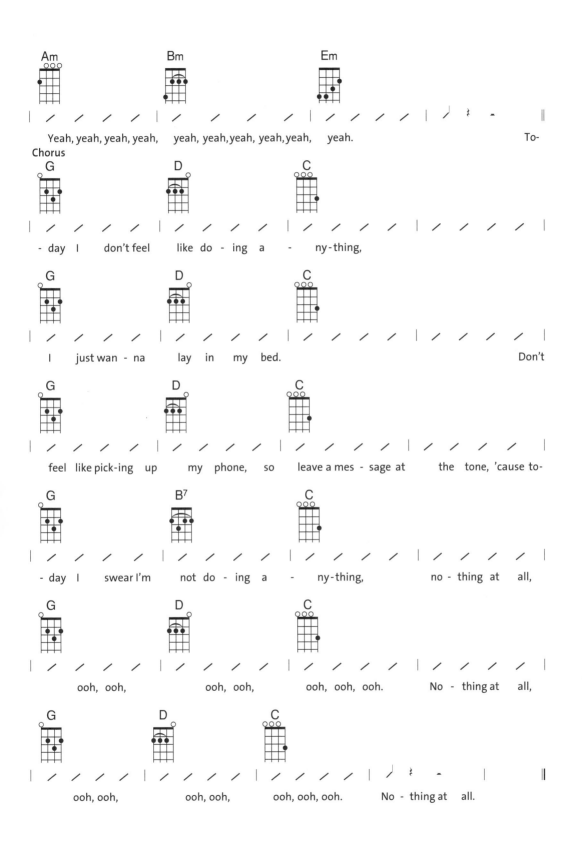

Am   Bm   Em

Yeah, yeah, yeah, yeah,   yeah, yeah, yeah, yeah, yeah,   yeah.   To-

Chorus

G   D   C

- day I   don't feel   like do - ing a   -   ny-thing,

G   D   C

I   just wan - na   lay in   my   bed.   Don't

G   D   C

feel like pick-ing up   my   phone,   so   leave a mes - sage at   the   tone, 'cause to-

G   B⁷   C

- day I   swear I'm   not do - ing a   -   ny-thing,   no - thing at   all,

G   D   C

ooh, ooh,   ooh, ooh,   ooh, ooh, ooh.   No - thing at   all,

G   D   C

ooh, ooh,   ooh, ooh,   ooh, ooh, ooh.   No - thing at   all.

She Began To Dance ("Match.com")

Words & Music by Matthew Pescod

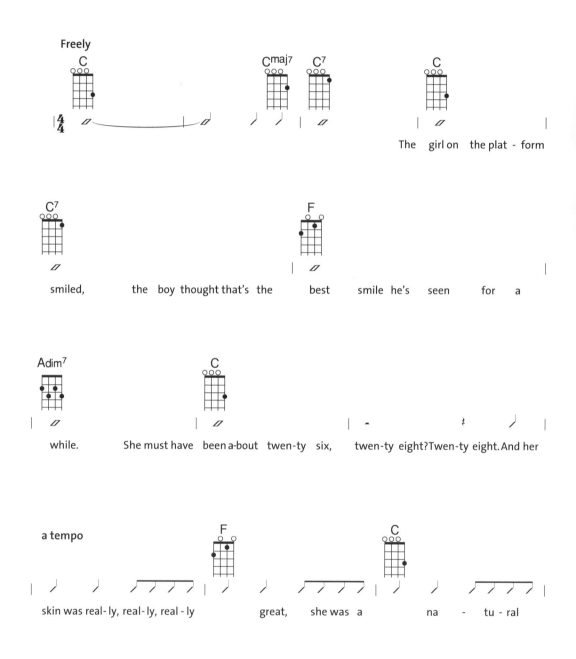

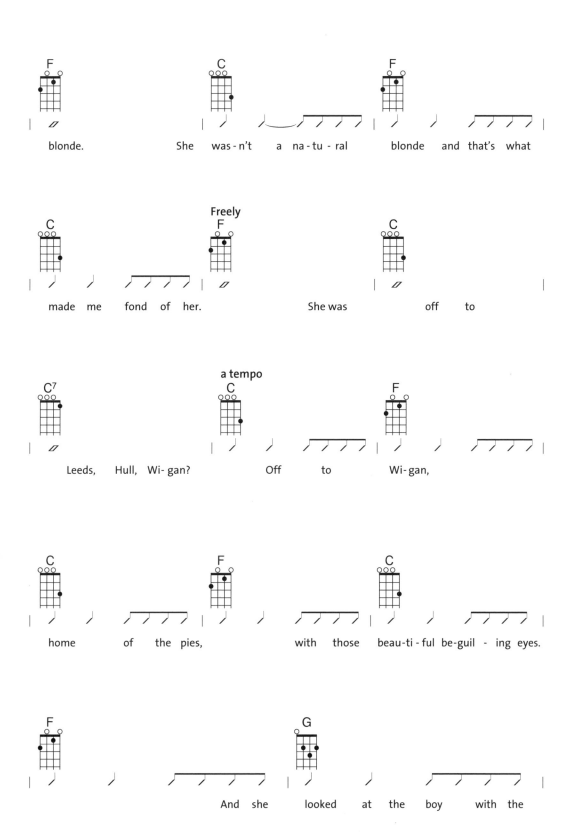

F

blonde.

C

She was-n't a na-tu-ral

F

blonde and that's what

C

made me fond of her.

Freely
F

She was

C

off to

C⁷

Leeds, Hull, Wi-gan?

a tempo
C

Off to

F

Wi-gan,

C

home of the pies,

F

with those

C

beau-ti-ful be-guil - ing eyes.

F

G

And she looked at the boy with the

63

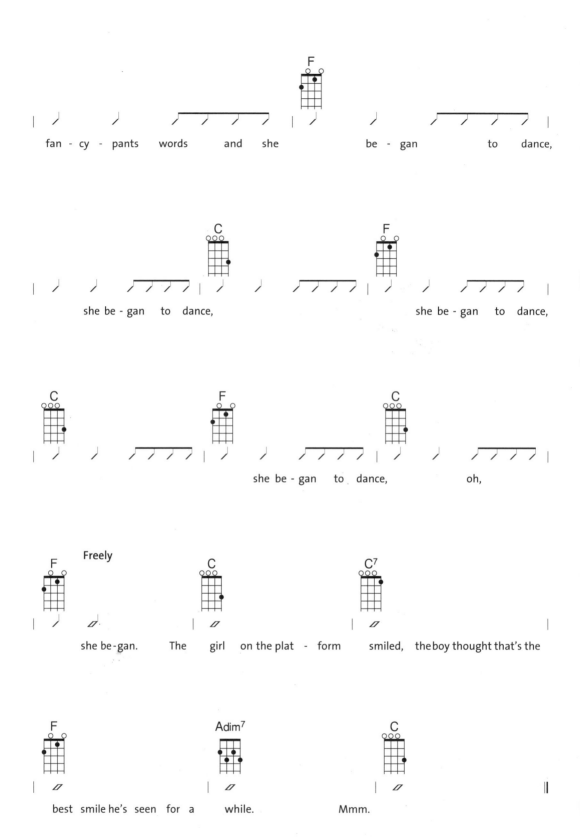

fan - cy - pants   words   and   she   be - gan   to   dance,

she be - gan   to   dance,   she be - gan   to   dance,

she be - gan   to . dance,   oh,

Freely

she be-gan.   The   girl   on the plat - form   smiled,   the boy thought that's the

best smile he's seen for a   while.   Mmm.